Tasmanian Tiger

Marion & Steve Isham

for Jim & Evelyn

We saw it when Dad stopped to change a flat tyre. It was in full view not ten metres away.

Ben and I had wandered along the road and paused by a clearing in the bush. Looking back, we could see Dad levering bolts.

Suddenly Ben caught his breath. There was our Tasmanian tiger. Its eyes held us for a long moment. Then quickly turning, it bounded away, displaying dark stripes.

made by both the quick and the DEAD can be seen clearly yet cannot be TOUCHED

the More you Take

the More you Leave Behind.

I raced to tell Dad and we all ran back to find some trace but the tiger was gone. It was then Dad suggested we watch out for footprints. If there really was a tiger, (how could he doubt us!) the footprints could prove it. Something very promising was already trampled, but we eventually found clear prints in the mud and photographed them.

We marked the spot well before we drove off and Ben told Dad how his class at school had made plaster casts from footprints.

"Couldn't we try that Dad?"

Dad thought photos would be enough but Ben pleaded that plaster would pick up details so in the end Dad agreed to stop at a shop in the next town.

Has Cities But No houses

forests But No trees

rivers But No fish

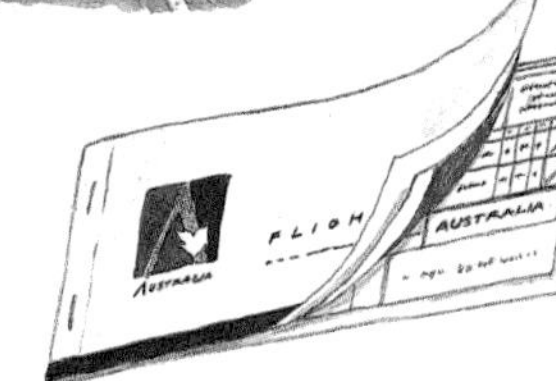

ENOUGH FOR ONE TOO MUCH FOR TWO AND NOTHING AT ALL FOR THREE...
MONEYCARD
JOHN A CITIZEN
1234567890
WIPE
Ultra
Yum
Quit
Zip 1kg
FILLA
500g
Xtra
DIP
200ml

A chat with the friendly shopkeeper while we were buying plaster ended with us telling our whole tiger story. We were too excited to be cautious. And it was near the end that a man wearing a black hat came in and overheard the last few words.

He looked at us with great interest as we left.

"Did you see how that man stared at us!"

ALWAYS DYING ALWAYS GIVING BIRTH
PLASTER
NOT FOR FLAMMABLE LIQUIDS

Returning to the site we mixed the plaster, poured it on a patch of footprints and got some good casts. It was another day before we were able to tell the story to a park ranger.

the Seed
One who sows
has great
Learning
White
the Field
Black
TASMANIAN BL
Eucalyptus globulus
Environ

She studied the casts for a long time. “They do look like the real thing. But don’t talk about this to anyone! The last thylacine died in 1936...”

“A lot of people will be looking for it.” I said.

“Yes, and that could be fatal. Leave it to me. I’ll need to look into this.”

“The secret’s safe with us. We won’t breathe a word,” we promised.

In another town, while we were buying T-shirts we got the idea of starting a collection of tiger souvenirs. That really set us off and we were scanning the shops when the man in the black hat reappeared. It was a shock to see him and a greater shock when he said, "Where did you see your Tasmanian tiger?"

"It was ... in ... in ... a shop." Ben managed to say.

Then we bolted.

asks no questions yet needs to be answered

He followed us into the shop.

“Would you please tell me about your tiger?” he asked.

We edged around a display case. Then standing near a table crammed with bric-a-brac, Ben said, “It’s ... it’s here somewhere.”

And there, to our utter amazement, was a tiger. The man looked from the postcard to our faces and I could see that he didn’t believe us.

He opened his mouth to speak, but we made hasty excuses and ran from the shop.

having neither TOP

nor BOTTOM yet

holding FLESH

blood and BONE.

The search for tigers was on. We found ...

USE ME WELL AND I AM EVERYBODY
SCRATCH MY BACK AND I AM NOBODY
SALAMANCA

UNDER THE bed SITS NOT alone. WITH long tongue lolling OUT A-WAITING FOR A BONE

Runs OVER fields ALL day

ONE WHO MADE IT DIDNT WANT IT ONE WHO BOUGHT IT DIDNT USE IT ONE WHO USED IT DIDNT KNOW IT
GLAZE
A Potter's Book
CD
B
BB
B

what ***FORCE*** or ***STRENGTH*** cannot

get through I with

gentle touch can do.

the less it is the more it is dread
AD 1823

I *tremble* at each BREATH of air

yet can HEAVIEST

BURDENS

bear

OUT AND ABOUT ALL DAY YET I ALWAYS AT HOME STAY

Light as a feather

Nothing in it, a strong man can't hold it more than a minute.

THEY COME WITHOUT BEING fetched BY DAY THEY ARE lost WITHOUT BEING stolen AT night

bridle or saddle across a

almost BLIND are made

to See without

THING I RIDE a~straddle

and those I ride

by help of me though

The day we left Tasmania we went back to see the ranger.

"There's someone I'd like you to meet," she said. "He studies thylacines. The timing is perfect. Let me introduce you."

"May I continue the search for your tiger?" grinned the man in the black hat.

Ben glanced at me. "He turned out to be OK!"

We both smiled our relief. "Of course you can," we said.

when first I appear I Seem mysterious yet when I'm explained I'm Nothing serious

Tassie Tiger
TASMANIAN TIGER